Love Unknown

A Cantata on the Passion and Resurrection of Jesus

Text by Edwin Le Grice

Music by
Malcolm Archer

We hope you enjoy the music in *Love Unknown*. Further copies are available from your local music or christian bookshop.

In case of difficulty, please contact the publisher direct by writing to:

The Sales Department
KEVIN MAYHEW LTD
Rattlesden
Bury St Edmunds
Suffolk IP30 0SZ

Phone   0449 737978
Fax   0449 737834
Access and Visa facilities are available for payment.
Please ask for our complete catalogue of outstanding Church Music.

The publishers wish to express their gratitude to Cambridge University Press for permission to use extracts from *New English Bible* © 1970 Oxford and Cambridge University Presses.

First published in 1992 by
KEVIN MAYHEW LTD
Rattlesden
Bury St Edmunds
Suffolk IP30 0SZ

© Copyright 1992 by Kevin Mayhew Ltd

ISBN 0 86209 214 0

Cover design by Graham Johnstone
Printed in Hong Kong by Colorcraft Limited

CONTENTS

Part 1   What Is Love?

1. Prelude

2. Love is from God
(Narrative)

When he saw him he was moved to pi-ty. He went up, ban-daged his wounds, bathed them with oil and wine, lift-ed him on-to his own beast, brought him to an inn, looked af-ter him, charged the inn-keep-er to

Man.

take care of him, took out two pence more.

3. I may speak with the tongues of men
(Song)

I may have faith strong e-nough to move a moun-tain,

but if I have no love I am no-thing.

I may dole out all I pos-sess or give my bo-dy to be burnt,

but if I have no love I am none the bet-ter.

Ped. (16')

11

4. Hear the words of Jesus
(Narrative)

Moderato (♩=80)

BARITONE

Hear the words of Je - sus: No man is wor - thy of me who does not take up his cross and walk in my foot - steps. By gain - ing his life a man will lose it. By los - ing his life for my sake he will gain it.

Ped.

Man.

mf cresc.

Ped.

5. Love is not feeling
(Chorus)

ten - der-ness, pas-sion and ten - der-ness stand wide a -

stand wide a - part. *dim.*

- part, (But do they?)

TENORS AND BASSES

mf

Love is not deeds, Saint Paul in - sists:

cresc.

feed - ing the hun - gry, the mar - tyred bo - dy burnt:

less.

can they?)
can they?)

Or is love both?

Heart drawn to heart, hand stretched to hand:

sa - cra-ment of touch?

Con-scious, de - li - be-rate

6. This is my commandment
(Responsory)

Tempo rubato
BARITONE SOLO

This is my com-mand-ment:

($\quarternote$=96) *mf*

S
A

That you love one a - no - ther.

T
B

mf

Freely
SOLO

1. There is no greater
   love than this, that
   a man lay down his   life for his friends.

2. You are my
   friends if you do   what I com-mand you.

3. I call you servants
   no longer: I have   called you friends.

   Glory to the Father
   and to the Son
   and to the   Ho - ly Spirit.

After each verse
($\quarternote$=96)
mf

S
A

Love one a - no - ther.

T
B

mf

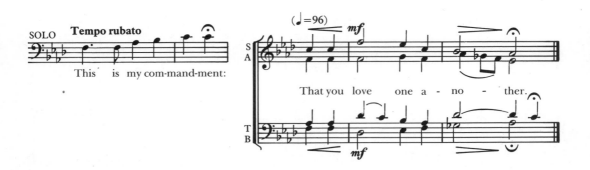

Tempo rubato
SOLO

This is my com-mand-ment:

($\quarternote$=96) *mf*

S
A

That you love one a - no - ther.

T
B

mf

7. My song is love unknown: Verse 1
(Congregational Hymn)

My song is love un – known, my Sa- viour's love to me: love to the love - less shown, that they might love - ly be. O who am I, that for my sake, my Lord should take frail flesh and die?

Part 2   Stepping Down

8. Jesus knew his hour had come
(Narrative)

Je-sus knew his hour had come. He had al-ways loved his own who were in the world. Now he was to show the full ex-tent of his love.

Du-ring sup-per, well aware that the Father had en-trust-ed ev-'ry thing to him and that he had come from God and was going back to God,

meno mosso (♩=76)
strict time
mf

he poured out wa — ter in - to a ba — sin

and be- gan to wash the dis - ci — ples' feet.

dim.

Più mosso (♩=100)
SOPRANO *mf*

The di - vine na — ture was his from the first.

He did not think to snatch at e - qua - li - ty with God

but made him self no-thing. As - sum-ing the na-ture of a slave bear -ing

hu - man like - ness re-vealed in hu-man shape, he

hum - bled him-self, he hum - bled him-self and in o - be - dience ac-

-cep-ted ev - en death— ev - en death on a cross.

9. Image of the eternal Father
(Congregational Hymn)

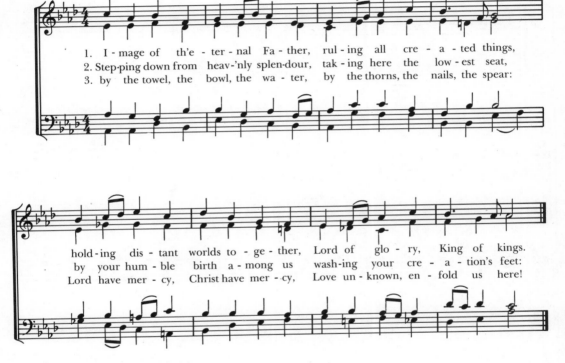

1. I - mage of th'e - ter - nal Fa - ther, rul - ing all cre - a - ted things,
2. Step-ping down from heav-'nly splen-dour, tak - ing here the low - est seat,
3. by the towel, the bowl, the wa - ter, by the thorns, the nails, the spear:

hold - ing dis - tant worlds to - ge - ther, Lord of glo - ry, King of kings.
by your hum - ble birth a - mong us wash - ing your cre - a - tion's feet:
Lord have mer - cy, Christ have mer - cy, Love un - known, en - fold us here!

Verses 1 and 2 in harmony; verse 3 in unison

10. Equality with Godhead
(Chorus)

place, emp-tied of glo-ry, ma — jes-ty and might,

be born the child of Ma — ry and at her

breast find rest?

Clothed in hu — mi — li — ty, child

of the sta — ble, how was he a —

-ble to learn o — be — dience,

to suf - - fer and to die,

that we re - joic - ing in his

glo - rious cross,

may ev - er more ac - claim

his ho -

- ly name?

11. Let this mind be in you
(Responsory)

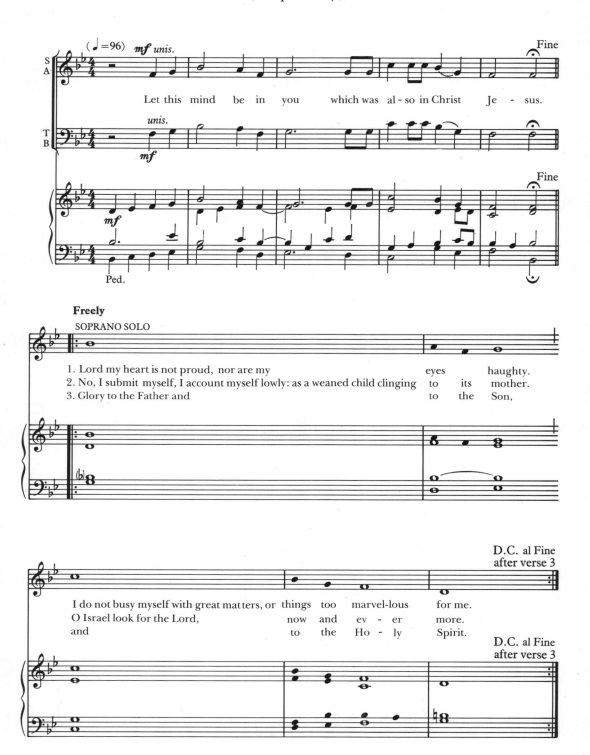

Let this mind be in you which was al-so in Christ Je - sus.

Freely

SOPRANO SOLO

1. Lord my heart is not proud, nor are my eyes haughty.
2. No, I submit myself, I account myself lowly: as a weaned child clinging to its mother.
3. Glory to the Father and to the Son,

I do not busy myself with great matters, or things too marvel-lous for me.
O Israel look for the Lord, now and ev - er more.
and to the Ho - ly Spirit.

D.C. al Fine
after verse 3

12. My song is love unknown: Verse 2
(Congregational Hymn)

He came from his blest throne, sal-va-tion to be-stow; but men made strange, and none the longed-for Christ would know. But O, my friend, my friend in-deed, who at my need his life did spend!

Part 3   The Sign of Jonah

13. Some of the elders
(Narrative)

Some of the el - ders and the Pha - ri - sees said. 'Mas - ter, Man.

we would like you to show us a sign'. Je - sus an - swered,

'It is a wick - ed and god-less ge - ne - ra - tion that asks for a sign:

and the on - ly sign that will be giv - en is the sign of the pro - phet

Jo - nah. At the judg-ment when this ge - ne - ra - tion is on

trial, the men of Ni - ne - veh will ap-pear a - gainst it and en-

-sure its con-dem - na - tion, for they re-pen-ted at the preach-ing of Jo - nah

and what is here is great – er than Jo - nah'.

Tempo rubato

SOPRANO SOLO

God did not bring up - on Ni - ne - veh the di - sas - ter

Man.

which he had threat-ened; Jo - nah was great-ly dis - pleased. He sat down out-side the ci - ty,

say - ing, 'This O Lord is what I feared'.

BARITONE SOLO

When they reached the

place of the skull, they cru - ci - fied Je - sus. Je - sus said,

'Fa - ther, for - give them for they know not what they do'.

Fa - ther, for - give them for they know not what they

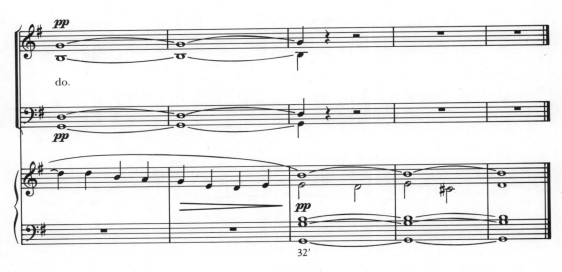

do.

14. What daring, comparing
(Chorus)

if we die?' 'Cru – ci – fy! Cru – fy!

Cru – ci – fy! Cru – ci – fy! Cru – – – –

– ci – fy!

SOPRANOS AND ALTOS
unis. *mp*

Af- ter three days, as the scrip - tures tell, won - der-ful - ly e- -jec - ted, won - der-ful - ly e - jec - ted from the bel - - ly of hell.

41

— ly of hell.

Scare-crow fi-gure out-side the ci — ty wall, scream-ing

ven-geance, ven-geance, ven — — — — —

Man.

44

15. God forbid
(Responsory)

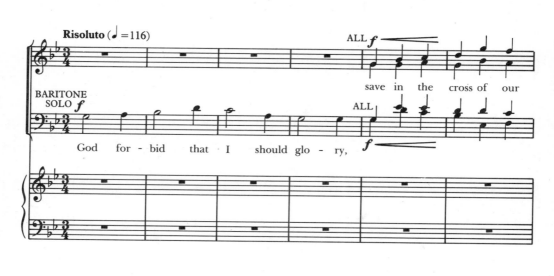

- nounce that right has won the day, I who am strong, am strong to save. God for - bid that I should glo - ry,

ALL
save in the cross of our Lord Je - sus Christ.

ALL

SOLO
He was des - pi -

-sed, he shrank from the sight of men, tor -

47

-men-ted and hum-bled by suf - f'ring. We des-

-pised him, held him of no ac-count. A thing from which men

turn their eyes. God for-bid that I should glo - ry,

save in the cross of our Lord Je-sus Christ.

Who gave a thought to his

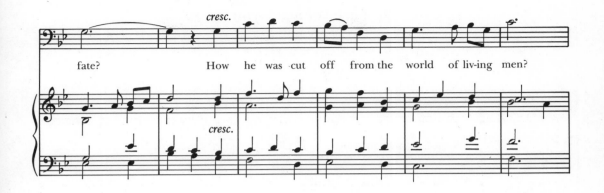

fate? How he was cut off from the world of liv-ing men?

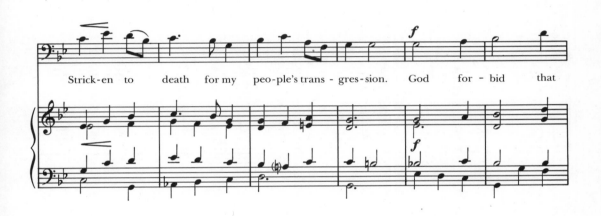

Strick-en to death for my peo-ple's trans-gres-sion. God for - bid that

save in the cross of our Lord Je - sus Christ.

I should glo - ry,

16. My song is love unknown: Verse 3
(Congregational Hymn)

Some - times they strew his way, and his sweet prai - ses sing; re - sound-ing all the day ho - san - nas to their King; then, 'Cru - ci - fy!' is all their breath, and for his death they thirst and cry.

Part 4 Wrestling In Prayer

17. Jacob came to a certain place
(Narrative)

Tempo rubato (♩ = 104)

BARITONE

Ja - cob came to a cer-tain place and stopped there for the night be-

Ped.

-cause the sun had set. Tak-ing one of the stones he made it a

pil-low for his head and lay down to sleep. He dreamt that he saw a

♩ =72 (in strict time)

Gt. flute 8'

Sw. flute 8'

Man.

lad-der which rest - ed on the ground with its top reach-ing to hea - ven,

Tempo rubato

and an-gels of God were go — — — ing up and down on it.

♩=66
(in strict time)

Tempo rubato
SOPRANO

The spi-rit sent

Je - sus a-way in-to the wil - der-ness and there he re - mained for for - ty

days, temp-ted by Sa - tan. He was a - mong wild beasts, and the

an - - - - gels wait - ed on him.

18. Bright angel hosts: Verses 1 and 2
(Congregational Hymn)

1. Bright an - gel hosts, who serve in realms a - bove, your
2. You mar - shalled for - ces of the powers of right, your

glo - rious wings dis - play: break through the clouds which veil God's heart of
or - dered ranks de - ploy to pierce the e - vil ar - mour of hell's

love: re - veal cre - a - tion's day.
might with shafts of heav - 'nly joy.

Verse 1 in harmony; verse 2 men only

53

19. Jacob was left alone
(Narrative)

Tempo rubato (♩=92)

BARITONE *mp*

Ja-cob was left a-lone and a man wres-tled with him there till day-break. When the

cresc.

man saw that he could not throw Ja - cob, he struck him in the hol-low of his thigh, so that

p

Ja - cob's hip was dis-lo - ca-ted as they wres-tled. The man said, 'Let me go, for

day is break-ing, but Ja-cob re - plied, 'I will not let you go un-less you

bless me'.   The man said, 'What is your name?'   and he an-swered 'Ja-cob'. The man said,

'Your name is no long-er Ja - cob but   Is - ra - el,   be-cause you strove with

God and man   and pre - vailed.   He gave him his bless-ing there,   and Ja - cob

called the place   'God's face',   be-cause he   said,   'I   have   seen God face to   face'.

20. This fear again
(Song)

rough-ness of wind-swept turf for bed: ban-ished from car-pet-ed

com - fort, do-mes - tic af - fec - - - tion,

gods - of - the - house - hold's shel - ter-ing pro-tec - tion,

phy - si-cally, men - tal - ly, mys - - ti-cally

out   on his   own.

But this   time   strug - gling, writh - ing,

fear - ful·ly flinch - ing from   fu - ry of at - tack:

in sa-vage bit-ter con - flict driv — — —

- ing the cruel as - sas - sin flat up-on his back:

dim.

bat - tling in vain, a - gain, a - gain,

to wrest dis - clo - sure of the sec - ret, sac-red

name; at - tain glo-ri-ous triumph-ant end to cru-el

a piacere
mf
f

striv - ing.

With sud-den, pain-ful shock he felt the ad - ver-sa - ry dis-place the hol-low of his thigh: heard a voice pro-claim, 'Is - ra-el, not Ja - cob is your name',

glimps - ing a face — 'God's

power - ful prince, with man you shall pre - vail'.

De - feat - ed, dazed,

halt - ing on hol - low thigh, The

sun rose on him, in a cloud - less de - sert

sky. He gave a cry: 'Pe - ni -el! God's

face! How love - ly

is this place!'

21. When Jesus reached the place
(Narrative)

Tempo rubato (♩=84)

BARITONE

When Je-sus reached the place, he said to his di - sci-ples, 'Pray that you may be spared the hour of test - ing'. He with-drew him - self from them a stone's throw, knelt down and be-gan to pray: 'Fa - ther, if it be thy will, take this cup a - way from me. Yet not my will but thine be done'.

Man.

Ped.

in strict time

mf

Slower (♪ =96/♩ =48)

And now there ap-peared an an - gel to him from heav'n bring-ing him

strength, and in the an-guish of his spi - rit he

prayed the more ur - gent - ly; and his sweat was like

rall.

clots of blood fall - ing to the ground.

22. Bright angel hosts: Verses 3 and 4
(Congregational Hymn)

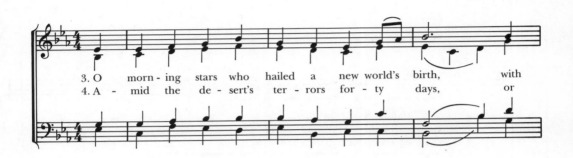

3. O morn - ing stars who hailed a new world's birth, with
4. A - mid the de - sert's ter - rors for - ty days, or

shouts of praise ac - claim be - yond th'un - fold - ing won - ders of the
in the gar - den's night, sur - round us with your sym - pho - ny of

earth the glo - ry of his name.
praise, God's mes - sen - gers of light.

Both verses in harmony

23. Count it all joy
(Responsory)

Freely
SOPRANO SOLO

1. Count it all joy when you fall into temp - ta - tion:
2. Out of the depths have I called to you, O Lord.
3. O let your ears consider well the voice of my suppli - ca - tion.
4. I wait for the Lord: my soul longs for him, and in his word is my hope.
   Glory to the Father and to the Son and to the Holy Spi - rit.

Repeat after each verse
♩=72

S
A

The try - ing of your faith works pa - tience.

T
B

24. My song is love unknown: Verse 4
(Congregational Hymn)

Part 5   Naked Truth

25. Prelude

26. The Lord called
(Narrative)

Adagio (♪=92)

BARITONE

The Lord called to the man and said to him, 'Where are you?'. He re-plied, 'I heard the sound as you were walk-ing in the gar-den, and I was a-fraid be-cause I was na-ked, and I hid my-self'. God an-swered, 'Who told you that you were na-ked?

(un poco più mosso)

Have you eat-en from the tree which I for - bade you?'

The time came for Ma-ry's ba-by to be born, and she gave birth to a son, her

Man.

first - born. She wrapped him in swad-dling clothes and laid him in a man - ger,

be - cause there was no room for them to lodge in the inn.

crown of thorns they placed it on his head, with a

reed in his right hand. Fall - ing on their knees be -

CHORUS (T.B.)
& BARITONE SOLO *f (mocking)*

-fore him they jeered at him: 'Hail, King of the

BARITONE
SOLO

Jews, hail, King of the Jews!' They

73

spat at him and used a cane to beat him a-bout the head;

slower

and when they had fi - nished their mo - cke ry, they led him a-

-way to be cru - ci - fied. Hav ing cru - ci - fied Je - sus, the

sol-diers took pos-ses-sion of his clothes and di - vi -ded them in - to four parts,

one for each sol - dier, leav-ing out the tu - nic. The tu - nic was seam-less, wo -

- ven in one piece through-out; so they said to one a - no - ther, 'We must not

tear this; let us toss for it'. Thus the text of the scrip-ture came true:

p soft reed

(***ppp***)

'They shared my gar-ments a-mong them and cast lots for my cloth - ing'.

27. Adam and Eve
(Chorus)

A-dam and Eve from E – den's gate   dri-ven by sword of

flame,   clo-thed with shame, with bruis-éd heel   and sweat of brow,

fal – len now,

fal - - len now!

Se - cond A - dam our lit - tle bro - ther

bare - ly born,

swad-dled in hay;

stripped of our sin, on Gol go tha's tree, you set us free, you set us free!

28. All those that see me
(Responsory)

In strict time (♩ =96)
BARITONE SOLO

All those that see me   laugh me to scorn: they shoot out their lips at me and wag their heads.

Verse

1. 'He trusted in the Lord, let him deliver him: let him deliver him if he de-lights in him.'

2. I can count all my bones: they stand staring and gazing upon me.
   They part my garments among them, and cast lots   for my clothing.

   Glory to the Father and to the Son and to the   Ho - ly Spirit.

Response after each verse

They shall look on him whom they have pierced.

29. My song is love unknown: Verse 5
(Congregational Hymn)

Why, what hath my Lord done? What makes this rage and spite? He made the lame to run, he gave the blind their sight. Sweet in - ju - ries! Yet they at these them - selves dis - please, and 'gainst him rise.

Part 6　Finished Work

30.　Prelude and Narrative

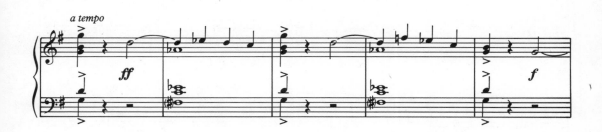

Tempo rubato (♩=96)

BARITONE

When the news came to our e-ne-mies that I, Ne-he-mi-ah, had re-built the walls of Je-ru-sa-lem— al-though I had not set up the doors in the gates— they sent an in-vi-ta-tion to come and con-fer with them. This was a ruse on their part. So I sent mes-sen-gers to them with this re-ply, 'I have im-por-tant

(Ped.)

work on my hands. I can-not come down. Why should the work be brought to a stand-still?'

They sent a si - mi - lar in - vi - ta-tion four times and each time I gave them the same an - swer:

Man.

'I have im-por - tant work on my hands: I can - not come down'.

Ped.

Faster
SOPRANO

The pass-ers-by hurled a - buse at Je - sus: they wagged their heads and cried,

Man.

In strict time (♩=96)

mp

'You would pull down the tem-ple, would you, and build it in three days? Come

mp

cresc.

Ped.

broadly

dim.

down from the cross and save your-self, if in-deed you are the Son of God'.

f

dim.

Tempo rubato

BARITONE

mf

So too the chief priests with the law-yers and el-ders mocked at him: 'He saved o-thers', they

mf

Man.

slower

(mocking)

f

mf

said, 'but he can-not save him-self. King of Is - ra-el in - deed! Let him

f

now come down from the cross then we will be - lieve him'.

From mid-day a dark-ness

fell ov-er the whole land which last-ed un-til three in the af - ter -

noon. And a-bout three Je - sus cried a - loud,

Deciso

'E - li, E - li, la - ma sa - bac - ta - ni?', which means:

Man.

Very slow

'My God, my God, why hast thou for - sak - en me?'

Ped.

'Let us see if E - li - jah will come to save him, will come to save him'.

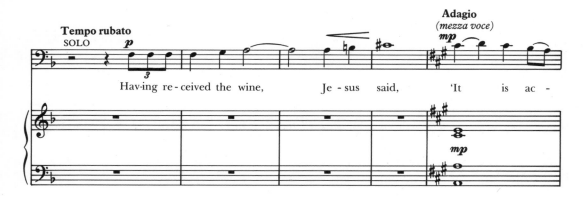

Hav-ing re - ceived the wine, Je - sus said, 'It is ac -

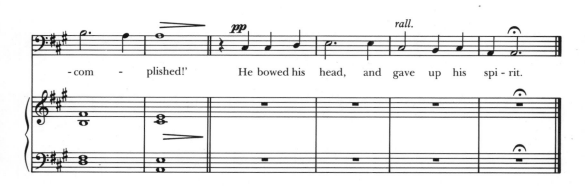

- com - plished!' He bowed his head, and gave up his spi - rit.

Silence should follow.

31. Great Son of God
(Congregational Hymn)

1. Great Son of God, you once on cal-v'ry's cross fought the long fight for truth and free-dom's sake, en-dured the scourge, the crown of thorns, the nails that fixed your youth-ful bo-dy to a stake. For six long hours you suf-fered sear-ing pain to set your cap-tive peo-ple free a-gain.

2. 'Give us a sign from heav'n', the peo-ple cried: 'If you are Christ, leap down, a-live and free. Who could ac-cept as Sa-viour one who died like some poor mis-creant skew-ered to a tree?' Lord Christ, our Sa-viour, you would not de-scend un-til your glo-rious work a-chieved its end.

3. 'My God, my God, where have you gone?' you called a-lone and help-less, will-ing still to share through all the gath-'ring gloom of Cal-va-ry, the depth of dy-ing sin-ners' deep des-pair. But then tri-um-phant, rea-dy now to die, 'The work is fi-nished!' was your glo-rious cry.

Verses 1 and 2 in harmony; verse 3 unison.

32. Incongruous images
(Song)

With menace (♩=60)

BARITONE

In - con - gruous i - ma-ges gro-

-tes - quely in-ter-twined: Ter - rors of de-

-lu - sion the reel - ing mind re - sists:

The slide in - to con - fu - sion, fac-ing with nailed

fists   phan - ta-sies of hor-ror: help - less,   hope-less,

blind.   Con-foun - ded, be - wil - dered,

twist - ed tor-tured mind: Eyes   vain - ly

scour - ing   the   dark   en - croach - ing   mists:

Yet through con·fu - sion your ring - ing voice per-

sists, pierc - ing death's dark - ness with vo - wels sharp, de-

+Sw. to Gt.

-fined. So when I

Gt.

Sw.

slide in - to the jaws of

death,   back to pri-mae-val   cha - os,

be - fore   the first cre - a - tion,   the

cry   that ov - er   Gol - go-tha   re - sound - ed   in

sharp - est tones of clear e-nun-ci - a - tion,   'My

mf   *cresc.*   *rit.*   *ff*

95

God! My God!' may

be my cry as well:

trust-ing in you, let me ne-ver

be con-found-ed.

33. Into thy hands
(Chorus)

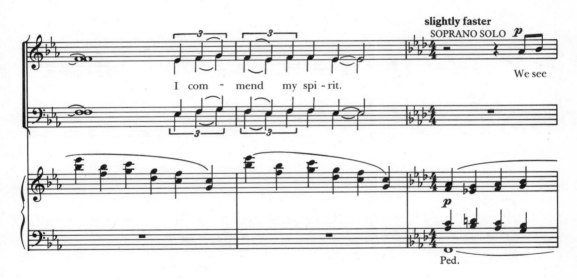

He be came o-be - dient un-to death, ev - en death

of the cross.

Tempo I

In-to thy hands O Lord I com - mend my spi - rit.

slightly faster
SOPRANO SOLO

He was tak - en from pri - son and from judge-ment. He has

poured out his soul un-to death. He was cut off out of the land of the

liv - ing for the trans - gres - sion of my peo - ple

was he strick - en.

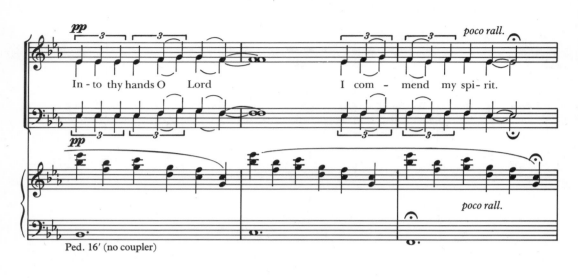

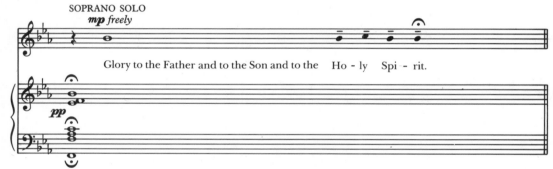

Glory to the Father and to the Son and to the Ho - ly Spi - rit.

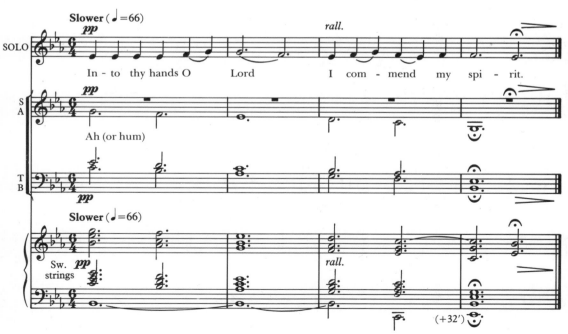

In - to thy hands O Lord I com - mend my spi - rit.

34. My song is love unknown: Verse 6
(Congregational Hymn)

They rise, and needs will have my dear Lord made a - way: a mur - de - rer they save, the Prince of Life they slay. Yet cheer - ful he to suff -'ring goes, that he his foes from thence might free.

Part 7   Dawn of New Life

35. Among those who went up to worship
(Narrative)

Strict tempo (♩=92)

plied, 'The hour has come for the Son of Man to be glo – ri –fied.

In truth, ve – ry truth I tell you, a grain of wheat re-mains a

so – li –ta –ry grain un – less it falls to the ground and

dies; but if it dies it bears a rich har –

Tempo rubato

-vest. The man who loves him-self is lost, but he who hates him

In strict time

-self in this world will be kept safe for e - ter - nal life.

If a - ny-one serves me, he must fol-low me; where I am, my

rall. ser - vant will be.'

slower (♩=72)
SOPRANO *ff*

Je - sus gave a loud cry

Gt. *ff*

faster (♩=144)

and breathed   his   last.

Sw. *mf cresc.*

Ped.

mf

At that mo - ment   the   cur-tain of the tem - ple was

f

torn   in two   from the top   to the bot - tom.

f

There was   an   earth - quake,   the   rocks split, the graves   o - pened

and ma-ny of God's peo-ple a-rose from sleep,   and

com - ing out of their graves af - ter his re - sur - rec - tion they

en - tered the ho - ly ci - ty,   where ma - ny

saw them.   And when the cen - tu - ri - on and his

Gt.

ff broadly

Man.

men who were keep-ing watch ov-er Je - sus saw the earth-quake and

all that was hap-pen-ing, they were filled with awe, and they

Ped.

Slow
BARITONE

said, 'Tru - ly this man, tru - ly this man,

tru - ly this man was the Son of God'.

36. Alive, not just in memory
(Song with Chorus)

SOLO: Splash of one peb - ble in this pre-sent pool cre -

S A (*p* unis.): Sing my tongue, the glo - rious

T B (*p* unis.):

-ates ex-pand-ing cir - - - cles spread-ing to e -

bat - tle, sing the

cresc.

cresc.

-ter - ni - ty.

Touch of the last, the dread af - fray;

mo - ment, sud - den smile or glance, a flash of o'er the cross, the vic - tor's tro - phy,

hu - mour, sad - - ness of a sigh,

sound the high tri - um - phal lay:

cry of de - light, of won - der

how the pains of death en -

Sw.   add

Gt.

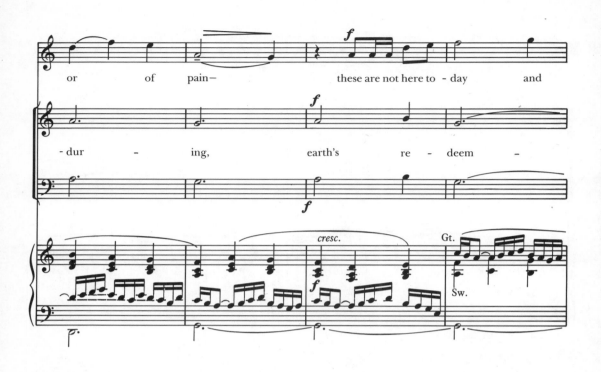

or of pain— these are not here to - day and

- dur - ing, earth's re - deem -

gone and that for ev - er's that,

- er won the

37. Lord, your voice in Eden's garden
(Congregational Hymn)

1. Lord, your voice in E - den's gar - den   in the cool of ev - 'ry day,
2. Here we meet you, ri - sen Sa - viour,   in the mar - vels of your earth:
3. In un - li - mi - ted for - give - ness   rea - dy to re - ceive and give,
4. From this earth to heav'n as - cend - ing   by the lad - der of your love,

e - choes still, a - mong the o - lives,   call - ing us to   watch and pray.
in the trust of   lit - tle child - ren   see the won - der   of your birth:
o - pen hand - ed,   o - pen heart - ed,   show your ser - vants how to live,
here your an - gels, Lord, sur - round us,   op - 'ning doors to   realms a - bove.

Christ, our glo - rious Eas - ter gard - 'ner,   list - 'ning dai - ly to your voice,
here in sweat of   dai - ly la - bour,   here in love of   man and wife,
bear - ing sin, en - dur - ing suff - 'ring,   shar - ing joy, ac - cept - ing pain,
Here, in still - ness of your pre - sence,   know - ing that we are your own,

in the life of   re - sur - rec - tion   may we here and   now re - joice.
here in strength of mind and bo - dy   share your re - sur - rec - tion life.
learn - ing, ri - sen Lord and Mas - ter,   how to die and   rise a - gain.
may the dawn of   re - sur - rec - tion   break up - on us,   Love Un - known.

Verse 1 in harmony; verse 2 women in unison; verse 3 men in unison; verse 4 in harmony

38. Behold, he is coming
(Responsory)

BARITONE SOLO

		with the clouds:
1. Behold he is coming		of the dead:
2. Christ was raised to life; the first fruits of the harvest		ev - er more:
3. Fear not, I am the first and the last and the living one; I died, and behold I am alive for		all things new:
4. I am the Alpha and the Omega, the beginning and the end; behold, I am making		Ho - ly Spirit:
Glory to the Father and to the Son and to the		

After each verse ♩=92

ev - 'ry eye shall see him, and a - mong them those who pierced him.

attacca

39. My song is love unknown: Verse 7
(Congregational Hymn)

Triumphantly (♩=100)

ORGAN

attacca

115

DESCANT

Here might I stay and sing, no sto-ry so di-

S A
ORGAN

Here might I stay and sing, no sto-ry so di-

T B

-vine; nev-er was love, dear King, nev-er was grief like

-vine; nev-er was love, dear King, nev-er was grief like

thine. This is my Friend, in whose sweet praise I

thine. This is my Friend, in whose sweet praise I

all my days could glad-ly spend. A - men.

Org.

all my days could glad-ly spend. A - men.

Org.

The view east from Bridge No. 37A, just after connection of the single-line chord. As can be seen, the former Up line is still *in situ* but now cut where the chord joins, the Down line being slued to connect. This became Shirebrook South Junction and the points installed became Shirebrook Junction No. 25 points. Access to Warsop Yard from this end is now not possible, and the sidings would become overgrown and disused for a period, before being used for wagon storage. Warsop Cottage farm is on the left of the view, with the headstocks of Warsop Colliery on the skyline. (*John. S. Gilks*)

The same view on 16 May 2014 as GBRf 66748 passes Shirebrook West Junction with 6B56 16.00 Thoresby Colliery to West Burton. Although Warsop Cottage Farm is still there, the trees on the lineside are so high the farm is not visible. (*Author's Collection*)

Bibliography

Anderson, P. and Cupit, J., *An Illustrated History of Mansfield's Railways* (Bedfordshire: Irwell Press, 2000)

Batty, S. R., *Rail Centres: Sheffield* (London: Ian Allan Ltd, 1984)

Cupit, J. and Taylor, W., *The Lancashire, Derbyshire and East Coast Railway* (Monmouthshire: Oakwood Press, 1988)

Dow, G., *Great Central Volume Three: Fay Sets the Pace, 1900–1922* (London: Ian Allan, 1965)

Grainger, K., *Scenes from the Past: 43 Sheffield Victoria to Chesterfield Central, The 'Derbyshire Lines' of the Manchester, Sheffield & Lincolnshire Railway Part One* (London: Foxline, 2002)

Little, L., *Langwith Junction, The Life and Times of a Railway Village* (Vesper Publications, 1995)

Vanns, M., *The Railways of Newark-on-Trent* (Oakwood Press, 1999)

Various issues of the Great Central Railway Society's *Forward* magazine

Various issues of *Great Central Link* magazine.

Various issues of *North East Derbyshire Industrial Archaeology Society Journal*.